# CONTENTS

# POLAR BEARS UNDER THREAT

IN NOVEMBER 2004, A STORY HIT THE HEADLINES THAT GAVE THE ISSUE OF GLOBAL WARMING A REAL VICTIM. DR LARA HANSEN, A CHIEF SCIENTIST AT THE WORLD WILDLIFE FUND (WWF), WARNED THAT IF **CLIMATE** CHANGE IS NOT BROUGHT UNDER CONTROL, POLAR BEARS WILL LOSE THEIR HUNTING GROUNDS AND CONSEQUENTLY BECOME EXTINCT BY THE END OF THE 21ST CENTURY.

## SEA ICE AND BEAR STARVATION

In the Arctic Circle, the region at the very top of Earth, an area of ocean called the **ice sheet** remains permanently frozen. During winter and spring, the sea surrounding the ice cap freezes and pushes up against the mainland coast. Polar bears hunt their primary prey, ringed seals, on the Arctic sea ice during this period – walking for many kilometres across the ice, or swimming from ice floe to ice floe. When the sea ice thaws in the summer, the bears are forced to come ashore and primarily live off stored fat. Today, according to a study by scientists from the

The Arctic ice melts earlier each year, driving hungry polar bears onto land and into contact with people, who hunt them.

21ST CENTURY SCIENCE

# GLOBAL
# WARMING

By Susie Hodge

Publisher: Melissa Fairley
Editor: Miranda Smith
Designer: Emma Randall
Production Controller: Ed Green
Production Manager: Suzy Kelly

ISBN-13: 978-1-84898-104-1 pbk

Copyright © *ticktock* Entertainment Ltd 2010
First published in Great Britain in 2010 by *ticktock* Entertainment Ltd,
The Old Sawmill, 103 Goods Station Road, Tunbridge Wells,
Kent, TN1 2DP

Printed in China
9 8 7 6 5 4 3 2 1

Picture credits (t=top; b=bottom; c=centre; OFC= outside front cover; OBC=outside back cover):

AFP/Getty Images: 48t, 52. Dr Juerg Alean/Science Photo Library: 22t, 22c. Peter Arnold, Inc/Alamy: 37b. BPPT/Handout/Reuters/Corbis: 32–33t. British Antarctic Survey/Science Photo Library: 41t. Climateprediction.net/Science Photo Library: 53b. Sue Cunningham Photographic/Alamy: 49. Mauro Fermariello/Science Photo Library: 30t. George Holton/Science Photo Library: 35t. iStock: 10–11t, 16–17, 42b. D. Kesling/OAR/National Undersea Research Program (NURP); Univ. of North Carolina – Wilmington: 17b. Christine Muschi/Reuters/Corbis: 55t. Chuck Nacke/Alamy: 51t. NASA, Goddard Institute For Space Studies/Science Photo Library: 39b. NASA/Goddard Space Flight Center Scientific Visualization Studio: 7t (both). NASA/Science Photo Library: 45b. NOAA Climate Program Office, NABOS 2006 Expedition: 28. NOAA/Science Photo Library: 32t. PhotoDisc: 20tr, 21tl, 27tl, 40t. Jenny E. Ross/Corbis: 5l. Rev. Ronald Royer/Science Photo Library: 12–13b. Victor de Schwanberg/Science Photo Library: 54b. Shutterstock: OFC, 1 all, 2 all, 4–5, 5r, 5r (background), 6l, 6–7b, 7r, 8–9, 10l, 11r, 11r (background), 11b, 12l, 13r, 14l, 14b, 14–15, 15r, 15r (background), 18–19 all, 20l, 21r, 21r (background), 22l, 23r, 23r (background), 24–25 all, 26 all, 27r, 30l, 31 all, 32l, 33r (background), 34l, 34–35b, 35r, 36 all, 37r, 37r (background), 38–39, 40l, 41r, 41r (background), 42l, 42–43, 43r, 43r (background), 44l, 44–45t, 45r, 45r (background), 46 all, 47r, 48l, 49r, 50–51, 52l, 52r, 54l, 55r, 56l, 56r, 56r (background), 58–59 all, 60l, 60–61b, 61r, 62l, 63r, 64l, OBC all. Charles H. Smith/US Fish and Wildlife Service: 47t. Pasquale Sorrentino/Science Photo Library: 29t. Volker Steger/Science Photo Library: 57b. George Steinmetz/ Science Photo Library: 9. Stringer/Brazil/Reuters/Corbis: 56t. Tim Venon/Tony Raddock, LTH NHS Trust/Science Photo Library: 60t.

Every effort has been made to trace copyright holders, and we apologize in advance for any omissions. We would be pleased to insert the appropriate acknowledgements in any subsequent edition of this publication.

NOTE TO READERS
The website addresses are correct at the time of publishing. However, due to the ever-changing nature of the Internet, websites and content may change. Some websites can contain links that are unsuitable for children. The publisher is not responsible for changes in content or website addresses. We advise that Internet searches should be supervised by an adult.

Canadian Wildlife Service (CWS), climate change is melting the sea ice earlier each year. This shortens the bears' hunting season and threatens them with starvation. Polar bears now have around three weeks less hunting time in the spring than they did 20 years ago. As a result, scientists say that summer weights for both male and female polar bears are declining and that females are giving birth to fewer cubs.

Scientists weigh an unconscious female polar bear. In peak condition, males weigh around 600kg and females 350kg.

# INVESTIGATING THE EVIDENCE: POLAR BEARS AND GLOBAL WARMING

**The investigation:** Canadian scientists hope to provide evidence that polar bears are losing weight year on year because they have less time to hunt on the Arctic ice as a result of global warming.

**The scientists:** A team led by Dr Nick Lunn from the Canadian Wildlife Service (CWS), with funding from the World Wildlife Fund (WWF).

**Collecting the evidence:** Dr Nick Lunn and his team fly by helicopter along the coast of Canada and Alaska, spotting polar bears on the sea ice. When they spot them, they land and the bears are tranquilized with a sedative, which is shot from a dart gun. Bears varying in age from 2–24 years old are measured (their age is gauged by the condition of their teeth), weighed and their overall condition recorded. Each bear is fitted with an ear tag that has a unique number.

**The conclusion:** New data is compared with old data in order to measure change. Each year the survey is repeated, forming a comprehensive record of the polar bears' changing physical condition. The team found that the Western Hudson Bay population is vulnerable to changes because they are near the southern limit of polar bear territory. These bears have on average weighed less and given birth to fewer cubs since 1981.

# WHAT IS GLOBAL WARMING?

For many years, environmentalists have warned that our planet is getting dangerously warmer. Gases that result from burning **fossil fuels**, such as **carbon dioxide**, sit high up in the Earth's **atmosphere**. As their name implies, these **greenhouse gases** act like the glass in a greenhouse, trapping the Sun's heat. Scientists believe that this **greenhouse effect** is warming the Earth and causing dramatic climate changes.

## MELTING ICE CAPS

Experts have long suspected that the warming Arctic temperatures, resulting from a build-up of greenhouse gases in the atmosphere, may cause the loss of Arctic sea ice. National Aeronautics and Space Administration (NASA ) researchers have recently analyzed a 20-year record of satellite measurements. In addition to the sea ice melting earlier each year, the findings show that the permanent ice sheet that covers the Arctic Ocean is slowly disappearing decade by decade.

The surface of the Earth absorbs some solar **radiation** and reflects some. Global warming means that the balance of what is absorbed is altered.

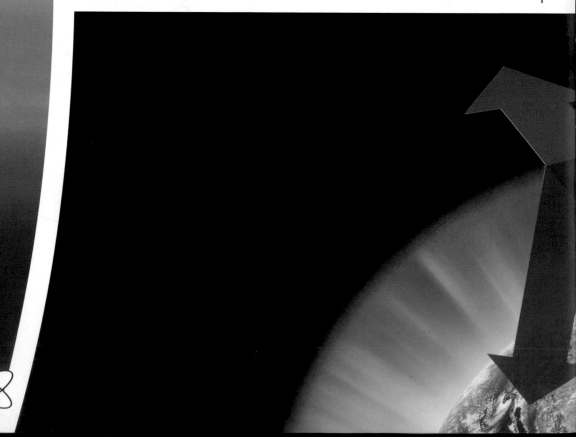

These images show the minimum sea-ice concentration in the Arctic Ocean for the years 1979 (top) and 2003 (above). The US Defense Meteorological Satellite Program collected the data to create the images.

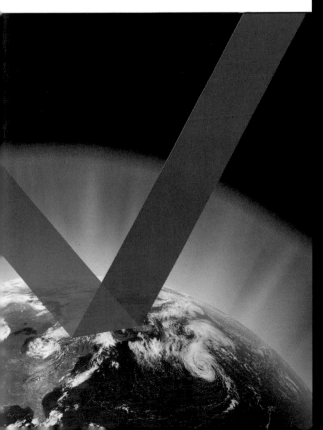

## A CAREER IN SCIENCE

Dr Josefino Comiso works for NASA's Goddard Space Flight Center in Maryland, USA. He mainly studies sea ice – ice that forms and floats in the ocean. Sea ice is different from glacial ice or ice sheets because it is saline (salty). After a few years, it becomes almost fresh and can be used as drinking water.

## A DAY IN THE LIFE OF ...

Since 1978, Dr Cosimo and his team have discovered that about 1.2 million square km of supposedly permanent ice has melted away. Dr Comiso's findings show that the permanent ice cover is melting at roughly three times the rate that scientists had thought – around ten per cent per decade. If the melting continues at this rate, the permanent ice sheet at the top of the Earth will have disappeared before the end of the 21st century. Arctic snow and ice help to control the Earth's temperature, keeping heat and moisture on land and in the oceans. The findings have implications for global climate patterns, and Dr Comiso aims to discover if these changes are associated with human activities.

## THE SCIENTIST SAYS...

"Climate changes are amplified in the Arctic because bright white ice reflects sunlight from [the] Earth's surface."

# CHAPTER ONE

# ATMOSPHERE

WRAPPED AROUND OUR PLANET IS A MIXTURE OF GASES CALLED THE ATMOSPHERE. THIS LAYER REACHES UP TO AROUND 700KM ABOVE THE EARTH AND MERGES INTO SPACE. WITHOUT IT, OUR PLANET WOULD BE TOO COLD FOR LIFE TO SURVIVE. THE ATMOSPHERE ABSORBS HEAT FROM THE SUN AND HOLDS IN WARMTH WHILE PROTECTING US FROM HARMFUL **ULTRAVIOLET** RAYS AND METEORITES. IT ALSO GIVES US AIR TO BREATHE AND WATER TO DRINK.

## THE ATMOSPHERE

Scientists divide the atmosphere into four layers. We live in the bottom layer called the **troposphere**, which extends for around 6km upwards. The troposphere contains three-quarters of all gases in the atmosphere, together with **water vapour** and dust. It is warmed by the Sun, but most of its heat is reflected off the ground. The air we breathe is part of the troposphere. More than 78 per cent of it is made up of nitrogen gas. Around 21 per cent is oxygen, which all living things need in order to survive. The remaining one per cent is made up of carbon dioxide, water vapour and tiny amounts of other gases such as argon, neon and ozone.

Observing atmospheric changes allows scientists to improve our understanding of the world and to predict future changes to the ozone layer.

Scientists in Antarctica launch a helium balloon into the atmosphere. These balloons ascend into the lower stratosphere and measure temperature, pressure and position every 15 minutes.

Above the troposphere is the **stratosphere**, which is warm and dry. The **mesosphere** lies beyond the stratosphere, and after that is the **thermosphere**.

## THE OZONE LAYER

Ozone gas occurs naturally in our atmosphere. Most of it lies in the stratosphere, forming a protective layer over us and absorbing some of the Sun's dangerous ultraviolet rays. The **ozone layer** is no longer as thick as it once was. Human-made gases, **CFCs** (chlorofluorocarbons), have been released into the atmosphere. It has now been discovered that the chlorine present in CFCs destroys the ozone and has contributed to the layer's depletion.

Scientists have warned that the tornadoes that occur in the central USA may be something that other areas of the world will experience if global warming continues to happen.

## WEATHER AND CLIMATE

Our planet has a huge range of climates, from icy to tropical, each affected by various factors, including the Sun, the movement of the oceans and ice sheets. The climate of a region is its average **weather** over a period of time and includes the measurement of all the weather experienced during that period. Long-term climate change can only be measured over years.

## CHANGES OVER TIME

Today, scientists say that many adverse impacts of global warming have started to occur, including floods, droughts, rising ocean temperatures and severe weather such as hurricanes and tornadoes. However, weather and climate are unpredictable. Between 1918 and 1940, before the world was heavily industrialized, there was a period of warming, and between 1940 and 1965, just when human emissions were increasing at their greatest rate, the climate cooled.

## THE HOTTEST DAY

In August 2003, many parts of Europe experienced the hottest weather since records began more than

100 years ago. The heatwave was linked to extraordinary weather in other parts of the world – including the worst drought on record in Australia and massive floods in the USA. The World Meteorological Organization (WMO) issued an alert in July 2003 warning that 'extreme weather events might increase' around the world. They linked a record number of wild weather events, such as tornadoes, to global warming.

Extreme weather conditions, often caused by global warming, can trigger floods.

# INVESTIGATING THE EVIDENCE: HEATWAVES AND GLOBAL WARMING

**The investigation:** Scientists look for evidence to support the theory that unusual heat levels are caused by global warming.

**The scientists:** Researchers at the UK's Hadley Centre for Climate Prediction and Research – one of the world's leading scientific groups – who are studying the effects of changing climates.

**Collecting the evidence:** Each year, these scientists produce a report assessing climate change. In 2004, for instance, the Hadley scientists reported on recent European heatwaves. They studied thermohaline circulation – how ocean currents carry warmth from the tropics to other locations. One current driven by thermohaline circulation is the **Gulf Stream,** which carries warm water from the Caribbean to the east coast of North America, crossing the Atlantic Ocean to Europe and causing warmer winters.

**The conclusion:** If the melting ice sheets affect the Gulf Stream, shutting the circulation down, the whole of the northern **hemisphere** could actually cool, and this would cause even greater problems than global warming.

# THE OCEAN'S EFFECTS

The oceans cover around 70 per cent of Earth's surface and contain roughly 97 per cent of its water supply. They absorb heat from the Sun. As water takes longer than land to heat up and cool down, coastal areas are warmed by warmer sea air during the winter and cooled by cooler sea air during the summer. Ocean currents also influence climate. They carry warm water from warm places to colder regions and heat up winds.

## THE WATER CYCLE

Some warm water **evaporates** from oceans, seas, lakes and rivers. Plants also lose water in the air through **transpiration**. Water vapour in the air eventually **condenses**, forming tiny droplets in clouds. When the clouds meet cool air over land, **precipitation** is triggered and water returns to the land (or sea) as rain, sleet or snow. Some soaks into the ground and is trapped between rock or clay layers, becoming groundwater. Most flows downhill, eventually returning to the oceans.

## EL NIÑO AND LA NIÑA

Some scientists believe that global warming is influencing weather patterns known as El Niño and La Niña. Every few years, a large area of warm water from the Pacific Ocean pushes

Unusual weather conditions cause unusual events. In 1998, the Death Valley desert in California, USA, flowered because of rainfall caused by the El Niño event in the Pacific.

▶ ▶  www.elnino.noaa.gov/

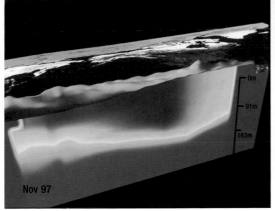

This model shows higher temperatures and sea levels in the Pacific Ocean during an El Niño event.

east to the coast of South America. This movement alters ocean currents, changes wind patterns and causes powerful storms and droughts across more than half the planet. It has been named El Niño, which means 'little boy' in Spanish. Each El Niño usually lasts for around 18 months after it begins. The reverse of El Niño is known as La Niña, meaning 'little girl', and occurs about half as often as El Niño. At the moment, no one is sure what causes El Niño and La Niña, and what makes some events stronger than others.

## A CAREER IN SCIENCE

Mark Cane of Columbia University, USA, has written nearly 200 papers on a broad range of topics in oceanography and climatology. In 1985, he and his colleague Stephen Zebiak pioneered a method of forecasting El Niño. The Zebiak–Cane model has been the main tool used by many researchers to enhance science's understanding of El Niño events.

## A DAY IN THE LIFE OF...

For over three decades, Dr Cane has focused on tropical oceanography, climate modelling, palaeoclimate, impacts of climate on society, El Niño and more. In developing his pioneering computer model with Stephen Zebiak, he successfully made the first physical forecasts of El Niño in 1985. With the pattern of powerful El Niños of 1982–3, 1997–8 and 2009, he has also worked extensively on the impact of El Niño on human activity, especially agriculture.

## THE SCIENTIST SAYS...

"We came to understand and predict El Niño and the Southern Oscillation (ENSO).... Over the years the Zebiak–Cane model has been the primary tool used by many investigators to enhance understanding of ENSO. Making predictions led to asking what to do with them. So I began to work on the impact of El Niño and other climate variability on human activity, especially agriculture and health."

## THE SUN

The most important influence on a region's climate is its proximity to the Sun. Locations on Earth that are nearest the Sun experience hot temperatures all the year round. The Earth's orbit around the Sun creates seasonal climates. In June, the northern hemisphere tilts towards the Sun and receives more sunshine and warmth than the southern hemisphere. By December, Earth has orbited halfway round the Sun. At this time, the southern hemisphere tilts towards the Sun and the northern hemisphere tilts away from it.

## EARTH'S CLIMATE

Earth's climate has changed dramatically since the planet began forming more than 4.5 billion years ago. There have been several ice ages, the last one ending about 15,000 years ago. So much water was frozen in vast ice sheets on land that the sea level was more than 100m lower than the current level, and ice covered most of North America and Northern Europe. Ice ages are believed to be caused by changes in Earth's orbit and its tilt towards the Sun. Scientists predict that another ice age will occur, possibly in the next 10,000 years. Various methods are used to gather climate data. Instruments measure temperature, precipitation, wind

The northern hemisphere of the Earth tilts towards the Sun in June, so it is summer in New York City, USA, and winter in Sydney, Australia.

speed and direction, and atmospheric pressure. Physical and biological data provide fossil evidence of past climatic conditions, and satellites monitor daily weather conditions and longer-term climate changes.

## GLACIERS RETREAT

**Glaciers** are found on every continent except Australia. Since 1850, glaciers have been shrinking, causing problems for animals and plants that depend on glacier water, and affecting the level of the oceans. Glacial retreat slowed and even reversed during 1950–80 as a slight global cooling occurred. However, since 1980, global warming has led to glacier retreat increasing rapidly, and many glaciers have disappeared.

A scientist monitors solar activity from a research base at the North Pole.

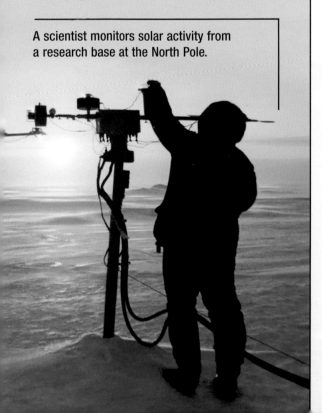

# INVESTIGATING THE EVIDENCE: OZONE DEPLETION

**The investigation:** The shrinking ozone layer is studied in detail to find out how it affects Earth's climate.

**The scientists:** A team from the National Oceanic and Atmospheric Administration (NOAA) of the USA.

**Collecting the evidence:** NOAA scientists measure changes in the ozone layer around the world over time. Laboratory investigations, atmospheric observations and other studies have produced an understanding of the ozone layer and its effect on ultraviolet radiation. Climate change and ozone depletion could be linked as ozone plays a vital role in shielding the Earth from ultraviolet light from the Sun. Ozone depletion occurs in many places but is most severe above the polar regions. These areas receive larger variations in the amount of sunlight than anywhere else on the planet.

**The conclusion:** NOAA sicentists have found that human-produced gases have caused the ozone 'hole' that has been occurring since the late 1970s. Ozone-friendly gases have now replaced the ozone-depleting gases. The scientists also measure these gases as they accumulate in the atmosphere to see if they affect the climate.

# CHAPTER TWO

# HEAT TRAP

THE GREENHOUSE EFFECT KEEPS THE PLANET WARM ENOUGH TO SUSTAIN LIFE, BUT IF THIS EFFECT INTENSIFIES, TEMPERATURE RISES COULD CAUSE PROBLEMS FOR ALL LIFE FORMS ON EARTH. IN RECENT YEARS, THE AMOUNTS OF CARBON DIOXIDE AND METHANE RELEASED INTO THE ATMOSPHERE HAVE INCREASED. THIS HAS ALTERED THE DELICATE BALANCE OF GASES IN THE AIR AND POSSIBLY INCREASED THE GREENHOUSE EFFECT.

The impact of global warming could have disastrous consequences. Scientists claim that even a 4°C rise would kill off 85 per cent of the Amazon rainforest.

## HEAT-TRAPPING GASES

The main greenhouse gas that occurs naturally is water vapour, which is mostly evaporated from rivers, lakes, seas and oceans, but also from plants and animals. Gases in the stratosphere trap any heat that escapes through water vapour. Carbon dioxide ($CO_2$) is the most important of these gases. Some natural events, such as volcanic eruptions, emit vast quantities of $CO_2$. As well as carbon dioxide, other gases from natural sources contribute to the greenhouse effect. For example, rotting vegetation in marshes and swamps releases methane, while tropical rainforests give off nitrogen oxide.

## UNDER THE SEA

Sediment is earth and rock that has built up in layers over time under oceans, seas, lakes and rivers. Over thousands of years, the layers become cemented together with other substances. Scientists can learn a lot about past climates by analyzing sedimentary layers. They collect and analyze sediment cores from lakes and bogs. They have found pollen (evidence of past vegetation changes), charcoal (evidence of a history of fires) and **algae** (evidence of past water-level and nutrient changes within the body of water they are investigating).

Scientists collect a core of sediment from the sea floor. They will take this back to the laboratory for analysis to find out about past climates.

# FOSSIL FUELS

Humans add to the greenhouse gases by using three fossil fuels: coal, oil and natural gas. Fossil fuels provide around 66 per cent of the world's total electrical power and 95 per cent of the planet's energy demands, including heating, transport and cooking. They are **non-renewable resources** – once we have burned them all, we will not be able to replenish them.

Over 85 per cent of the industrialized world's energy needs are met by the burning of fossil fuels.

## FORMATION

Fossil fuels were formed about 286–380 million years ago during the Carboniferous period, before the time of the dinosaurs. The land then was covered with swamps, trees and leafy plants. As the plants died, they sank into the ground and eventually formed layers of peat. Sand, rocks, clay and other minerals covered the peat and squeezed all the water out of it. After millions of years, this turned into coal, oil and natural gas.

## COAL

Coal is a hard, black rock-like substance. It is made up of carbon, hydrogen, oxygen, nitrogen and some sulphur. There are three main types of coal: anthracite, bituminous and lignite. Anthracite is the hardest and has more carbon. Lignite is the softest and low in carbon. Bituminous is in between.

▶▶ www.energyquest.ca.gov/story/chapter08.html

## OIL

The ancient Egyptians used oil as a medicine for wounds and in lamps to provide light. In North America, Native Americans used oil as medicine and to waterproof their canoes. Oil (like natural gas) is found under the ground between folds of rock.

## NATURAL GAS

Some time between 6000 and 200 BCE, the first discoveries of natural gas were made in Iran. The gas is composed mainly of methane.

Thick, black crude oil extracted from wells drilled on oil rigs (below) is taken to refineries where it is used to make products such as soap, fertilizer, clothes and plastic.

## A CAREER IN SCIENCE

James Zachos is Professor of Earth and Planetary Sciences at the University of California, Santa Cruz, USA. Among many other projects, he measures the chemical compositions of fossils in order to reconstruct past changes in the oceans.

## A DAY IN THE LIFE OF...

Professor Zachos and his team look at what created long- and short-term changes in global climate. They drill deep into sediment under the Pacific and Atlantic oceans to collect data. This has given them new insights into the amount of natural greenhouse gases that were released into the atmosphere in the past. Professor Zachos has discovered that, about 55 million years ago, the widespread release of methane and carbon dioxide caused temperatures to increase by around 5°C. The first mammals evolved at around the same time, but it is not clear whether there is any link.

## THE SCIENTIST SAYS ...

"Current human activity is releasing greenhouse gases around 30 times faster than ever before. The emissions that caused this past episode of global warming probably lasted 10,000 years. By burning fossil fuels, we are likely to emit the same amount over the next 30 years."

Levels of carbon dioxide have risen rapidly in the past 200 years because of discharge from rapid forest burning in order to clear the land for farming (above).

## HUMAN-MADE GREENHOUSE GASES

Developed countries have been using fossil fuels since the **Industrial Revolution** took place in the 19th century. The consumption of these fuels has nearly doubled every 20 years since 1900. By burning fossil fuels and cutting down trees, we release carbon dioxide back into the atmosphere, where it can remain for up to 200 years.

## TREES AND FORESTS

**Deforestation** also adds carbon dioxide to the air. When wood decays, it releases carbon slowly, but when it burns, most of the carbon escapes quickly in the form of carbon dioxide. Every year, the world's rainforests are being destroyed at an alarming rate as people clear the land so they can farm it or sell the wood for housing, crops and industry.

Half the world's rainforest has already been wiped out, and it is estimated that one square kilometre is destroyed every 2.5 minutes. Experts say we are losing at least

▸▸ www.rainforestinfo.org.au/background/causes.htm

Large areas of rainforest are cleared for only a few logs, and heavy machinery causes great damage.

137 plant, insect and animal **species** every day through deforestation.

On the other hand, living trees absorb carbon dioxide from the atmosphere and store it, releasing oxygen back into the atmosphere. With fewer trees, less carbon dioxide is removed from the air. The $CO_2$ levels in the atmosphere are currently at the highest since records began. However, it has been discovered that even in forests that have been left untouched, the effects of extra carbon dioxide are changing the environment, and causing some trees and vegetation to grow stronger.

# INVESTIGATING THE EVIDENCE: TREES AND CARBON DIOXIDE

**The investigation:** Scientists hoped to show that extra carbon dioxide in the atmosphere strengthens some trees.

**The scientists:** Biologist William Laurance and a team from the Smithsonian Tropical Research Institute in Panama.

**Collecting the evidence:** The team has spent 20 years investigating around 32,000 trees in undisturbed forests in central Amazon, South America. They identified nearly 1,300 tree species in 18 one-hectare study plots and repeatedly examined and measured each tree over time. The data allowed them to assess changes in the different species.

**The conclusion:** The growth of large trees has sped up over the past 20 years, while smaller trees have slowed. Levels of carbon dioxide have risen by 30 per cent in 200 years. The scientists suspect that the rising carbon-dioxide levels fertilize the rainforests and increase competition for light, water and nutrients in the soil. So the fast-growing trees are outpacing the smaller ones.

In 1994, the Steingletscher glacier in Switzerland looked like this. The ice forms from compacted snowfall, and wears away the rock beneath as it moves slowly forwards.

In 2006, the Steingletscher glacier in Switzerland looked like this. Global warming in recent years has accelerated the rate at which glaciers worldwide are disappearing.

# THE DISCOVERY OF GLOBAL WARMING

In 1824, a French mathematician and physicist, Jean Baptiste Joseph Fourier, first came up with the idea of the greenhouse effect. He compared Earth's atmosphere to a giant bell jar, suggesting that gases within the atmosphere help to trap some of the Sun's heat as it reflects off the planet's surface.

## MORE BREAKTHROUGHS

In 1896, a Swedish scientist, Svante Arrhenius, claimed that as people burned fossil fuels, the carbon dioxide released raised the planet's average temperature. By the 1950s, scientists discovered that the build-up of carbon dioxide in the atmosphere could cause global warming, and that the level of the gas was rising each year. Human activity was putting dust and smog particles into the atmosphere, which could block sunlight and cool the world. The scientists discovered that levels of other gases were rising, increasing global warming and damaging the atmosphere's protective ozone layer. By the late 1970s, global temperatures appeared to be rising rapidly, and international panels of scientists were warning that people should take steps to reduce emissions.

## RISING LEVELS

In November 2005, the scientific journal *Nature* announced that the amount of $CO_2$ in the atmosphere was higher than it had been for thousands of years. Another study reported in the same journal claimed that for the last past 150 years, sea levels have been rising twice as fast as in previous centuries. Scientists calculate that they are currently rising at 2mm per year as a result of heat expansion and glacier melt, both caused by recent increases in average global temperatures.

## INVESTIGATING THE EVIDENCE: DANGER IN THE ARCTIC

**The investigation:** Scientists have reported that humans have not reduced their carbon footprint on the Earth. This will possibly lead to a release of methane – a gas so powerful that it has the power to destroy the planet. The scientists say Arctic $CO_2$ levels are growing at an unprecedented rate.

**The scientists:** Johan Strom is Professor of Atmospheric Physics at the government-funded Norwegian Polar Institute, which collected the data. He and other scientists have worked with the Zeppelin research station on Svalbard, in northern Norway.

**Collecting the evidence:** Scientists have collected data that suggest that the main greenhouse gas, $CO_2$, is increasing in the atmosphere at an alarming rate. Levels at the Zeppelin research station on Svalbard, northern Norway, tend to be higher than the global average, but scientists say the levels they have measured are unprecedented even for that location.

**The conclusion:** Johan Strom says these are the highest figures in 50 years. It is not the level of $CO_2$ that is the problem, because the Earth will adapt. What is worrying is the speed of change, which is much faster than 10–20 years ago.

Coral reefs are some of the most beautiful of all the marine habitats. The corals provide shelter for many animals, including sponges, fish, crustaceans and turtles.

## ACIDIFYING OCEANS

The world's oceans are becoming more acidic as they take up some of our carbon-dioxide emissions. The oceans have taken up half of the $CO_2$ produced over the past 200 years – and when $CO_2$ reacts with seawater, it produces carbonic acid.

## LIMESTONE

Acidic oceans are dangerous for the many marine organisms – including mussels, clams, oysters and corals – that extract calcium carbonate from seawater to make their shells and bones. When the organisms die, their shells and bones accumulate on the seabed. Wave actions break them into smaller fragments, forming carbonate sand or mud. Over millions of years, the sediments may harden into limestone. Chalk is a type of limestone formed of the shells of microscopic animals, and it is more difficult to make chalk under acidic conditions. By 2065, there will no ocean regions where conditions allow corals to make calcium carbonate.

▶▶ http://kids.nceas.ucsb.edu/

# CORAL REEFS

Brightly coloured **coral reefs** are made up of living colonies of tiny animals called coral polyps. Although coral reefs can be as hard as rock, they are extremely sensitive to changes in temperature and pH – a measure of acidity – and will die off. If there are fewer creatures with calcium shells and skeletons, the current levels of fish in our seas will drop.

If ocean waters become too warm, corals will become more vulnerable to disease and death.

## A CAREER IN SCIENCE

Professor Katherine Richardson is a **marine ecologist** at the University of Copenhagen, Denmark. She studies ocean life and the marine environment, and monitors the natural ocean systems. Her focus is on the importance of biological processes in the ocean for the absorption of $CO_2$ from the atmosphere.

## A DAY IN THE LIFE OF ...

In 2006, Professor Richardson and her team studied the exchange of carbon between the atmosphere and the oceans. Because the seas contain 50 times more carbon than Earth's atmosphere, the scientists investigated what happens to the extra $CO_2$ that people put into the atmosphere through the burning of fossil fuels and deforestation. The scientists do not believe that the oceans will continue to take up so much $CO_2$, and they are building a global picture of carbon exchange so that they can predict climate change in the future.

## THE SCIENTIST SAYS ...

"Marine creatures do humanity a great service by absorbing half the carbon dioxide we create. If we wipe them out, that process will stop. We are altering the entire chemistry of the oceans without any idea of the consequences."

Carbon dioxide, propane and butane are all used as aerosol spray-can propellants. These greenhouse gases contribute to global warming and are bad for the environment.

## DANGEROUS EMISSIONS

There is considerable debate about the role that humans play in changing global climate. Some people argue that natural processes, such as volcanic eruptions and the Earth's tilt, are more of a threat to the atmosphere than the gases released.

## GASES CAUSED BY HUMANS

Since people started farming, growing crops and decaying vegetables have given off large quantities of methane.
But then in the 1950s, CFCs (see page 9) were added to the list of greenhouse gases. As well as being produced from coolants in refrigerators and air conditioners, CFCs used to be released from **aerosol** cans and certain types of foam packaging. Although the quantities of CFCs entering the atmosphere have been a lot less than other greenhouse gases, their effects are not fully understood. Some scientists believe that they might even cool the atmosphere.

Dust and ash in the atmosphere can block sunlight, lowering average global temperatures.

# NATURAL HAZARDS

Natural events, such as shifting ocean currents, changes in the amount of solar radiation reaching Earth and volcanic eruptions, can affect the climate. For example, volcanic eruptions can cause cooling by sending huge clouds of sulphur dioxide, water vapour, dust and ash into the atmosphere, partially blocking the Sun's rays. The volcanic activity may last only a few days, but it can affect the climate for years afterwards.

The amount and duration of the cooling of the climate depends on the quantity and size of the dust particles thrown out.

## A CAREER IN SCIENCE

Dr Drew Shindell is a climatologist with NASA's Goddard Institute for Space Studies in New York City, USA. In 2004, he was presented with a Scientific American Top 50 Scientist Award. His research is concerned with global climate change, climate variability and atmospheric chemistry. He investigates chemical changes such as the depletion of the ozone layer, climate change and the connections between the two.

## A DAY IN THE LIFE OF ...

Among other things, Dr Shindell and his team study the effects of short-lived gases and natural emissions from volcanoes, as well as investigating solar variations on climate. The scientists have been surprised to discover that ozone is a much bigger contributor to Arctic warming than originally thought. In the stratosphere, ozone helps to shield Earth from damaging solar radiation, but close to the ground, it can cause respiratory problems, harm crops and contribute to global warming.

## THE SCIENTIST SAYS ...

"We thought ozone was a minor player, but our new findings show that in the Arctic, ozone is responsible for up to 50 per cent of the warming. It was a big surprise."

# CHAPTER THREE

# A WINDOW TO HISTORY

HUMANS HAVE ONLY KEPT ACCURATE RECORDS OF WEATHER AND CLIMATE CONDITIONS FOR THE PAST 150 YEARS. TO UNDERSTAND CLIMATE CHANGES FURTHER BACK IN TIME, RESEARCH TEAMS BRAVE SOME OF THE WORLD'S COLDEST TEMPERATURES AND HARSHEST WINDS TO DRILL ICE SAMPLES, OR CORES. THESE PROVIDE SCIENTISTS WITH AN IMPORTANT WINDOW INTO THE PAST.

Ice core samples collected from Antarctica (below) and the Arctic are stored at −36°C.

THE PAST AND THE FUTURE

# ICE CORING IN ANTARCTICA

An ice core is a cylinder of ice about 15cm in diameter. Cores are collected by drilling deep into the ice. They are brought to the surface in lengths of about 3m. Working for the European Project for Ice Coring in Antarctica (EPICA), Dr Heinz Miller, geophysicist, and his team of researchers from ten European countries have drilled below the Antarctic surface right down to the **bedrock** under the ice. They have recovered, piece by piece, a 3km-long ice core that contains a climate record dating back one million years. Every 2.5cm represents one season's ice formation.

# ANCIENT WEATHER

As snow falls, it picks up chemicals and particles of matter from the atmosphere. Old snow turns to ice underneath, trapping tiny pockets of air. Snowfalls dating back many hundreds of thousands of years are frozen on the continent of Antarctica, forming a chronological record of the Earth's climate. The gases, chemicals and particles trapped in the ice and air pockets allow scientists to see how the climate responded to variations of greenhouse gases in the past.

A researcher tests samples from an Antarctic ice core. She is using equipment that can establish the composition of the air trapped in the ice.

# ICE-CORE ANALYSIS

When the ice cores are analyzed, the concentrations of gases such as carbon dioxide, hydrogen, oxygen and methane reveal the length of ice ages and periods of higher global temperatures. Scientists can compare our current climate and atmospheric make-up to past ages and make predictions about what to expect in the future.

Ice-core analysis is helping scientists to work out which global climate changes have been caused naturally and which have been caused by human impact. Many scientists say that human fossil fuel consumption is altering the Earth's climate, but the extent of that change remains a subject of debate.

A researcher uses a microscope to count the tree rings in a log from a silver fir tree. Rings correspond to half-years and allow the age of the tree to be calculated.

## SECRETS OF THE TREES

Some scientists study tree rings to learn about climates. Many trees are hundreds of years old, so tree rings can provide information about climates never before recorded.

### COUNTING RINGS

Rings of different shades form within tree trunks. Each shade corresponds to a period of growth by the tree. Rings are lighter during late spring and early summer, when trees grow quickly, and darker during late summer and early autumn, when growth is slower. This means that a light and dark ring together represent one year. The rings are counted to calculate the age of a tree, and growth patterns reveal the conditions that the tree has lived through.

▶▶ http://web.utk.edu/~grissino/

## CROSS-SECTIONS AND CORES

Scientists read tree rings in either a cross-section or in a core taken from the trunk. Cross-sections are used to read dead trees, while cores are used for living trees. To extract a core, an instrument is drilled into the trunk of a tree to remove a thin piece of wood that shows the rings. Using this method, the rings can be read without killing the tree.

In 2001, scientists researching tree rings in alpine forests in Mongolia worked out that temperatures in that region may be at their highest levels during the 21st century.

## INVESTIGATING THE EVIDENCE: TREES AND GLOBAL WARMING

**The investigation:** Scientists study tree rings in order to provide evidence of climate change over centuries or millennia – before records were first made.

**The scientists:** A team including Dr Gordon Jacoby and Dr Rosanne D'Arrigo from the Tree-Ring Laboratory at Columbia University's Lamont-Doherty Earth Observatory in New York, USA.

**Collecting the evidence:** The scientists analyzed tree rings in ancient Siberian pine trees in the mountains of west-central Mongolia, Asia. The team worked out annual temperatures dating from 262 CE to the present day.

**The conclusion:** The findings have helped to fill in a large gap in climate data from what is one of the more remote regions of the world – few records of past climates exist for northern Asia. The team found that, on average, tree-ring widths have been getting wider – and the global climate warmer – since the mid-1800s. The results suggest that temperatures in Mongolia reached their peak in the 20th century. The evidence gathered shows that the accumulation of greenhouse gases during this time is significant.

A photograph taken by the Nimbus 5 weather satellite shows a severe storm building in the Bering Sea off the Kamchatka Peninsular, Russia.

## PIECING IT TOGETHER

Meteorologists have used instruments to record changes in temperature, rainfall and air pressure at weather stations for more than 300 years. These include thermometers, rain gauges and barometers.

## EYES IN THE SKY

Since 1960, scientists have also used satellites to understand how the Earth's atmosphere functions.

Satellites provide a global picture of conditions on the Earth's surface, including remote areas. They allow meteorologists to forecast weather patterns more accurately. Images of the planet can be downloaded to weather stations every 30 minutes.

## BALLOONS AND BUOYS

To find information about the troposphere, meteorologists use an instrument called a **radiosonde**, which is carried up into the air by a weather balloon. It measures changes in temperature, pressure and humidity. A radio transmitter beams the data back to a weather

This buoy in the sea off the coast of Sumatra is part of a tsumani early warning system.

station, where a computer records it. At an altitude of about 30km, the balloon bursts and a parachute carries the radiosonde back to Earth. Meteorologists use a special aerial to track each radiosonde and measure wind speed and direction at different altitudes. This is known as a **rawinsonde**. Radiosonde and rawinsonde observations are made every 12 hours. Ships also report on weather conditions at sea. Some launch weather balloons and others release ocean **buoys** that record and transmit information about weather and other changes at sea level.

# INVESTIGATING THE EVIDENCE: CLIMATE CHANGE AND POLAR ICE

**The investigation:** Satellite observations, together with information about past and present climate changes, can help predict future changes.

**The scientists:** Dr Edward Hanna is a lecturer in climate change at the Department of Geography, University of Sheffield, UK. He often works with scientists in the USA (including NASA), Belgium and Denmark.

**Collecting the evidence:** Using glaciological and climatic instruments, including aircraft laser surveys and satellite data, Dr Hanna can work out the present-day size of the Greenland ice sheet and its contribution to global sea-level changes. The satellites detect heat and microwaves emitted naturally by the Earth's surface, so melting of the ice sheet can be detected.

**The conclusion:** Greenland has warmed by 2–3°C since the early 1990s, which has contributed to the increased melting of the ice since then. Some of these changes are likely to be due to rising greenhouse gases caused by human activity.

# CONTROLLING GLOBAL WARMING

Whether humans cause global warming is one of today's most controversial subjects. There are many reasons why scientists disagree on this topic. Despite all the research, the exact causes of climate change and the warming of the planet are difficult to prove.

## IS CO$_2$ THE CULPRIT?

Once carbon dioxide is released into the atmosphere, it remains there for about 100 years. CO$_2$ is created in different ways. As well as the burning of fossil fuels and deforestation, it is also created naturally, when humans and other animals breathe out or when vegetation decays. Fossil-fuel burning has increased massively as the world's population has tripled over the last century. Most of the CO$_2$ in the atmosphere is the result of this increase.

## DESTROYING EARTH'S LUNGS

All scientists agree that deforestation is causing imbalances in the climate and environment. Tropical rainforests once covered 14 per cent of Earth's land surface; now they cover a mere six per cent. Rainforests have been called 'the lungs of Earth', because trees

▶▶ http://kids.mongabay.com/lesson_plans/lisa_algee/deforestation.html

Within a few years of being cleared, rainforest land becomes unfertile and farmers have to move on.

absorb carbon dioxide and release oxygen into the atmosphere. The destruction of rainforests upsets this balance, with more carbon dioxide left in the atmosphere and less oxygen released. As trees are burned, even more $CO_2$ is released. It is estimated that one-third to one-fifth of the $CO_2$ in the atmosphere comes from rainforest destruction.

Most of the electricity used to power cities is generated by using fossil fuels such as coal.

## A CAREER IN SCIENCE

Dr Ted Gaten is the Principal Experimental Officer in the Department of Biology at the University of Leicester, UK.

## A DAY IN THE LIFE OF...

Dr Gaten was part of the team aboard the Royal Research Ship *James Clark Ross* in the Antarctic Ocean. The team aimed to establish why krill are declining in numbers in the most rapidly warming place on the planet. He and his colleagues, including Dr Ezio Rosato and Professor Charalambos Kyriacou from the University of Leicester, Department of Genetics and Dr Geraint Tarling from the British Antarctic Survey in Cambridge, investigated what determines krill behaviour and how this, in turn, impacts climate change.

## THE SCIENTIST SAYS ...

"Antarctic krill are the most abundant species of animal on the planet. However, recent research has shown that their numbers in the Antarctic Ocean have been drastically reduced; particularly in the Scotia Sea.... Krill are the principal diet of most of the animals that define the Antarctic oceanic **ecosystem**.... It is their importance to the ecosystem and their decline in response to global warming that has led to an increased interest in their behaviour and in the genetics underlying that behaviour."

Plants need sunlight, water, nutrients in the soil and the right temperatures in order to grow. It is important to understand the role that rising $CO_2$ levels may have on plant growth or there may be food shortages in the future.

## A NATURAL OCCURRENCE

Many scientists believe that climate change is a natural phenomenon and that because the annual amount of carbon dioxide entering the atmosphere from fossil-fuel emissions is only three per cent of the natural turnover, there is no reason to worry. They also point out that climate change has occurred throughout history, long before humans burned fossil fuels, and that the natural geological process can balance things out.

## FROM ICE TO WARMTH

The last ice age, which covered most of Northern Europe and North America with glaciers and most of the Amazon area in South America with open savannah, began to come to an end some 15,000 years ago. Natural climate change began melting glaciers, raising the world's sea levels by around 100m, while extra rainfall stimulated the growth of the rainforests in the Amazon basin. With some setbacks, warming continued until much of the now ice-free areas were covered with forests, locking in carbon dioxide and producing new, rich soils full of carbon.

## CHANGES OVER TIME

In medieval times, northern European temperatures were comparable to those today and agriculture thrived. Then the **Little Ice Age**, from around 1400 to 1900, caused many people to die of ague (malaria), and Viking settlements in Greenland were wiped out. From 1915 to 1945, there was a rise of 0.4°C, countered in the following 20 years by a fall of 0.2°C. During the rest of the 20th century, there was a rise of 0.4°C, making an overall increase of only 0.6°C over the century.

Scientists point out that if all the carbon dioxide was removed from the atmosphere, the temperature would fall by 10°C. But, without carbon dioxide, there would be no **photosynthesis** to encourage plant growth and so no food. Increases in temperature are responsible for increases in atmospheric $CO_2$ levels, not the other way round.

---

Woolly mammoths were well adapted to the cold climate of the last ice age 150,000 years ago.

## INVESTIGATING THE EVIDENCE: HUMAN ACTIVITY AND GLOBAL WARMING

**The investigation:** Scientists are working to study the relationship between human activities and global warming.

**The scientists:** Climatologist Dr Geoff Jenkins and other scientists from the Hadley Centre for Climate Prediction and Research in the UK.

**Collecting the evidence:** Dr Jenkins and his team feed collected data on the causes of climate change, such as greenhouse gases, output from the Sun and volcano emissions, into computers for analysis. The results indicated that, particularly over the past 30 or 40 years, most of the warming has been caused by human activities.

**The conclusion:** There has been a large surge in global temperature since the mid-1970s, and a substantial part of that may be caused by human activity. Using records from ice cores, tree rings and other sources, Dr Jenkins and his team have established that over the previous 1,000 years or so, that level of temperature rise did not occur. Dr Jenkins believes that people cause global warming – but that we have the power to control it.

# CHAPTER FOUR

# MEASURING CHANGE

TO UNDERSTAND HOW THE EARTH'S CLIMATE WORKS AND TO PREDICT FUTURE CLIMATES, SCIENTISTS USE POWERFUL COMPUTER PROGRAMS CALLED CLIMATE MODELS OR COMPUTER MODELS. SCIENTISTS FEED DATA INTO THE MODELS, BUT THIS DATA IS OFTEN BASED ON EXTREMELY DIFFICULT TO RECORD MEASUREMENTS, SO THE RESULTS ARE NOT COMPLETELY ACCURATE. BECAUSE OF THIS, SOME PEOPLE QUESTION THE VALUE OF THE MODELS.

## CLOUD FORMATION

Richard Lindzen, a professor of meteorology in the Department of Earth, Atmospheric and Planetary Sciences at the Massachusetts Institute of Technology (MIT), USA, believes that climate models do not properly account for the physics of cloud formation. He thinks that, as a result, the climate models exaggerate the warming effects of carbon dioxide. He says, "It is a complicated issue how [the] Earth's climate changes; it has changed dramatically in the past – change has been the norm in climate, and we've had models in recent years that can't explain any of these major changes. Some models can't explain even shorter-term changes."

These computer-generated images show the projected increase in global surface air temperature from 1965 to 2050. They were made by the Global Climate Model of NASA's Goddard Institute for Space Studies. They show how the planet will warm up if the emission of greenhouse gases, such as carbon dioxide, methane and CFCs, continue to increase at current rates.

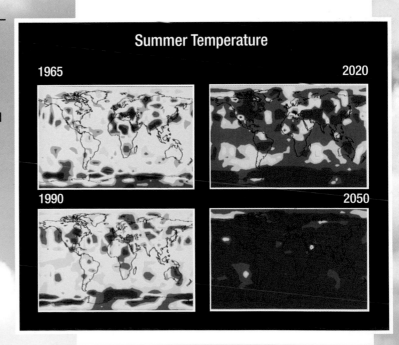

**Summer Temperature**

1965

2020

1990

2050

By burning fossil fuels to power our cars, we are putting more $CO_2$ as well as tiny airborne particles of soot, ash, sulphur compounds and other pollutants into the atmosphere.

## WARMING WARNING

The Intergovernmental Panel on Climate Change (IPCC) is made up of top climatologists from 60 nations. It was formed in 1988 by members of the United Nations Environmental Programme (UNEP) and World Meteorological Organization (WMO) to gain a better understanding of climate change. Since then, the IPCC has investigated various aspects of global warming.

## AEROSOLS

Many climate models now include clouds and tiny particles in the air, known as aerosols. Some aerosols come from natural sources, such as volcanoes, vegetation and sea spray. Others come from fossil-fuel burning and other human activities. Aerosols created by humans account for about ten per cent of the total amount in our atmosphere, with most concentrated in the northern hemisphere. Scientists are unsure whether aerosols are warming or cooling Earth, but they are important pieces of the global climate puzzle.

## GLOBAL DIMMING

Global dimming is when less solar energy reaches Earth. It appears to be caused by air pollution from fossil fuels, cars,

A researcher sets up a recorder on Alexander Island, Antarctica, to measure sunshine.

power plants and fires. This pollution reflects sunlight back into space, preventing it from reaching Earth's surface. The pollution also enters clouds, where it leads to the formation of smaller droplets, which make the clouds brighter and longer lasting. Scientists are worried that by shielding the oceans from the full power of the Sun, dimming may disrupt the world's rainfall pattern. Global dimming was first discovered by Gerry Stanhill, an English scientist working in Israel. Stanhill compared Israeli sunlight records from the 1950s with more recent ones and was astonished to find a large fall in solar radiation. It now appears that global warming caused by greenhouse gases is being counterbalanced by the cooling effect of global dimming.

## A CAREER IN SCIENCE

Professor Joanna Haigh is an atmospheric physicist in the Department of Space and Atmospheric Physics at Imperial College, London, in the UK. She investigates how atmospheric elements, including gases and clouds, absorb and scatter radiation emitted by the Sun.

## A DAY IN THE LIFE OF ...

Much of Professor Haigh's work on climate and climate change is carried out using computer models of the atmosphere and oceans. She says that the only way that it is possible to simulate the recent warming with climate models is by including greenhouse gases. To try to see how recent warming has been produced, greenhouse gas increases have to be put in the model. Using approximations each about 200km square by 2km deep, the climate model takes huge amounts of computer time to run, so the experiments have to be designed extremely carefully.

## THE SCIENTIST SAYS ...

"This is important research because it helps us to understand how climate has changed in the past and how much of the recent global warming is due to natural factors. I am hoping to be able to explain how small changes in the Sun's radiation can show up in climate records at different places across the globe."

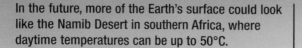

In the future, more of the Earth's surface could look like the Namib Desert in southern Africa, where daytime temperatures can be up to 50°C.

## HOT, HOT, HOT

Since humans began keeping records, Earth's climate has been fairly stable. According to researchers, the planet will become much hotter over the next century, and there is a 90 per cent chance that average temperatures will increase by 1.4–5.8°C by 2100. This is greater than any change in the last 10,000 years. It could cause sea levels to rise by 15–95cm, trigger extreme weather conditions such as floods, droughts, heatwaves and hurricanes, and contribute to plant and animal extinctions. The IPCC have said that even if emissions stopped increasing by 2100, the climate would continue to warm up until at least the 22nd century.

If Earth's temperatures rise, this could cause unpredictable extreme weather conditions, including droughts and floods.

www.theweatherchannelkids.com/climate-code/climate-close-up/extreme-weather/

## CRUCIAL CLOUDS

Clouds play a vital role in regulating temperature. They reflect solar radiation back into space and reduce heat loss in a similar way to the greenhouse effect. However, these effects depend on the depth, thickness and dimensions of the clouds, whether they are made up of water or ice and the size of their particles. Thick, watery cumulus clouds shield the atmosphere from incoming solar radiation by reflecting much of it back into space. Thin, icy cirrus clouds are poor sunshields but efficient insulators, trapping energy rising from Earth's warmed surface. Through clouds, Earth may be much less sensitive to the warming effects of rising levels of greenhouse gases in the atmosphere, although many scientists warn that we should not rely on them to save us from the effects of climate change.

## INVESTIGATING THE EVIDENCE: HURRICANES AND GLOBAL WARMING

**The investigation:** A recent study revealed that the number of strong hurricanes worldwide has nearly doubled over the past 35 years, and the shift occurred as global sea-surface temperatures became warmer.

**The scientist:** Kerry Emanuel of the Massachusetts Institute of Technology (MIT), USA, is an atmospheric scientist specializing in tropical meteorology and climate. He is also a leading hurricane expert.

**Collecting the evidence:** Dr Emanuel's work in has allowed him to model Earth's atmosphere and predict what will happen with hurricanes in the future. He says, "The energy released by the average hurricane seems to have increased by around 70 per cent in the past 30 years or so."

**The conclusion:** Dr Emanuel says that current and future global warming may increase the destructiveness of hurricanes. Although they are not occurring more than they have in the past, those that are occurring are far more intense.

The Arctic tundra (above) has subsoil that is permafrost. There is also permafrost tundra covering a vast stretch of land across Siberia in Russia, Alaska and Canada.

## FORECASTING THE EFFECTS

As scientists investigate the causes of global warming and the effects of climate, they often come up with surprising results. In 2001, the American Meteorological Society (AMS) published a headline-grabbing study. It stated that the Pacific Ocean could open a 'heat vent' above it, releasing enough energy into space to reduce future climate warming caused by the build-up of greenhouse gases in the atmosphere. Scientists noticed that high clouds over the western Pacific seem to decrease when the sea-surface temperatures are warmer, allowing heat to escape and keeping the oceans cool. Researchers analyzed satellite observations over a vast ocean region stretching from Australia and Japan to Hawaii. If this outlet is proved, it could significantly reduce estimates of anticipated global warming.

## MELTING PERMAFROST

Certain countries with particularly cold climates have **permafrost** – permanently frozen ground. If the permafrost thaws, structures built on it become unsafe, local wildlife is endangered and greenhouse gases could be released from the soil. Scientists believe permafrost may start melting three times faster than expected. No one knows if global warming causes it to melt, but it concerns scientists that warming could be increased by it. Merritt Turetsky, from Michigan State University, USA, led a study across a large

▶▶ www.amnh.org/exhibitions/climatechange/?section=ice&page=permafrost

## INVESTIGATING THE EVIDENCE: THE MELTING PERMAFROST AND GAS RELEASE

region of Canada, expecting to find that the thaw would trigger a release of greenhouse gases from carbon that has been locked away in the soil for thousands of years. His findings were surprising. The release of additional carbon is stimulating more plant growth, absorbing the carbon dioxide. However, the report cautions that melting permafrost results in flooding, which increases methane emissions. Methane is even more powerful than carbon dioxide and has a greater ability to trap heat in Earth's atmosphere.

This map shows the concentration of methane (red) in the stratosphere in 2004.

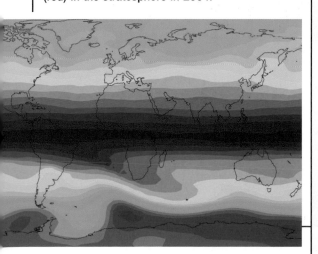

**The investigation:** Scientists want to provide evidence that melting permafrost releases carbon dioxide from soil.

**The scientist:** Dr David Lawrence of the US National Center for Atmospheric Research (NCAR) in Colorado and his team.

**Collecting the evidence:** Using computer models, Dr Lawrence led a study at the National Snow and Ice Data Center (NSIDC) into the thawing of permafrost. Expressing his concern that the Arctic region's soils are believed to hold about 30 per cent of all the carbon stored in the world's soil, he gave a warning: "Our study suggests that if sea ice continues to contract rapidly over the next several years, Arctic land warming and permafrost thaw are likely to accelerate. An important, unresolved question is how the delicate balance of life in the Arctic will respond to such a rapid warming."

**The conclusion:** Dr Lawrence is concerned that the permafrost seems likely to continue to retreat rapidly, which could cause accelerating coastal **erosion** and an increase of methane emissions.

## PREDICTING PROBLEMS

Most scientists agree on the changes and problems that rising temperatures could cause, including rising sea levels and the extinction of many plants and animals.

## FLOODS AND POLLUTION

The seas rose by about 18cm in the 20th century. One prediction claims that along with melting glaciers and ice sheets, oceans could rise at least another 50cm over the course of the 21st century. Another estimate says that by 2050, 150 million people in countries such as the Netherlands, India and Bangladesh could be homeless because of rising water levels. Riverbanks could burst, leading to local flooding, and coastal marshes that are habitats for fish and other marine life could be destroyed. Underground, rising sea levels may carry saltwater inland and pollute freshwater wells used by millions.

## GASPING FOR AIR

In November 2005, a headline announced that rising temperatures are threatening fish. Normally, fish metabolisms speed up in warmer

In the Gulf of Alaska in 1993, as fish moved into cooler waters, around 120,000 seabirds starved to death, as they were unable to dive deep enough to reach their relocated prey.

The golden toad of Costa Rica's cloud forests has not been seen since the 1980s, probably because of global warming.

water, but poor food supplies slow their growth and reproduction rates. Fish filter oxygen from water, but as temperatures rise, the amount of oxygen dissolved in water gets less. Whole populations of fish could move to cooler waters, leaving other fish-dependent species starving.

## SPECIES DESTROYED

Scientists have warned that one million species – equivalent to one-quarter of the world's plant and animal life – could be extinct within the next 50 years if steps are not taken to slow down global warming. Climate change kills plants and animals by causing stress and making them more susceptible to infection. Global warming destroys and diminishes their habitats. In the past, changing conditions occurred over thousands of years, but now the climate is altering rapidly. Already some species seem to have died out.

## A CAREER IN SCIENCE

Dr Nathalie Pettorelli is a Research Fellow at the Institute of Zoology at London Zoo in the UK.

## A DAY IN THE LIFE OF...

Dr Pettorelli uses satellites to help predict which species are under threat of extinction due to global warming. She uses photographs from space to study the vegetation available for wild animals to eat. She can show the impact of climate change on great wilderness areas and predict which species may be worse affected if the temperature rises and the grassland becomes a desert. Animals that rely on the vegetation include elephants, bushbuck and antelope and, indirectly, carnivores such as lions and cheetahs.

## THE SCIENTIST SAYS...

"This is a really important step forward in helping to determine conservation priorities in a changing climate. Even though we were unable to correct for several factors such as poaching intensity, predator density or soil nutrient status, we were still able to report a relationship between satellite indices and wildlife abundance. This suggests that the underlying relationship between satellite data and abundance might be even stronger than is apparent from initial analysis."

Children wade through flood waters after the cyclone Nargis hit their village in Myanmar in 2008. This was the worst natural disaster in the history of that country.

## HUMAN HEALTH

Global warming could affect human health adversely in several ways. Initially, in the northern hemisphere, warmer climates may reduce winter ailments and epidemics of flu.

## PLANTS AND FOOD

It is debatable whether pollen-producing plants will thrive or decline in warmer weather. If the plants flourish, the incidence of allergic diseases such as hay fever and **asthma** could rise. Drier soils are projected for many areas, which could cause stunted growth in vegetation, and deplete our supplies of vitamin-giving foods. More frequent and intense droughts are of the greatest concern and would severely affect food production.

## EXTREME WEATHER

If predictions for more extreme weather conditions happen, hurricanes, tornadoes and other weather disasters could leave people without clean water to drink. If food and water sources are

▶▶ http://epa.gov/globalwarming/kids/bigdeal.html

badly affected, malnutrition will increase and immunity decrease. There may be great danger in the way that pests and diseases respond to such climate changes. Also, the thinning ozone layer could let in more ultraviolet radiation, which causes skin cancer. This weakens the immune system, making people more vulnerable to disease. High temperatures place additional stress on the body, and heatwaves can lead to many deaths.

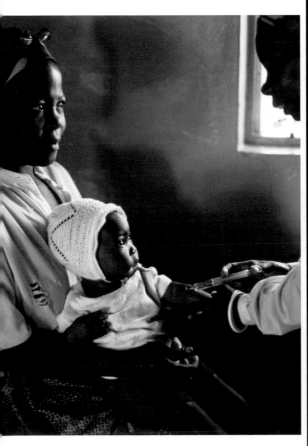

It is possible to give injections to immunize people against certain diseases, but it takes time and money to develop the vaccines.

## A CAREER IN SCIENCE

Dr John Harte is a professor of environmental science at the University of California, Berkeley, USA.

## A DAY IN THE LIFE OF ...

Dr Harte has been studying the effects of a warming planet for nearly 30 years. By simulating a warmer world over a contained area – he has selected the state of Colorado – Dr Harte is 'looking into the future'. He says that our current climate models are underestimating the magnitude of future warming. He predicts the planet will experience drought conditions, the reduction of water supplies and rises in sea levels, which could lead to the loss of entire island nations in the South Pacific. 'Killer' heatwaves, with longer periods at hotter temperatures than we have ever experienced, will occur. These will make life very uncomfortable and unhealthy for people all over the planet.

## A SCIENTIST SAYS ...

"The experiment is telling us about how ecosystems respond to climate change and how those ecosystem responses may accelerate global warming, and thus bring about greater sea level rise, and more intense storms, droughts and all the other problems associated with global warming. Thus the experiment suggests that it is especially urgent that we address the problem of controlling fossil-fuel consumption."

# CHAPTER FIVE

# TAKING ACTION

MANY PEOPLE BELIEVE THAT GLOBAL WARMING LEADS TO EXTREME WEATHER CONDITIONS. BUT IF GLOBAL WARMING IS THE CULPRIT AND IS CAUSED BY HUMAN ACTIVITY, HOW ARE GOVERNMENTS AND BUSINESSES HELPING? AND, IN PARTICULAR, WHAT ARE THEY DOING DURING NATURAL DISASTERS?

## TAKING RESPONSIBILITY

As the Earth's atmosphere warms, it generates longer droughts, more intense rain, more frequent heatwaves and more severe storms. Warm ocean temperatures can trigger these extremes, so global warming is often blamed. In July 2005, the worst drought on record set off wildfires in Spain and Portugal, left water levels in France at their lowest in 30 years and caused a lethal heatwave in Arizona, USA, that killed more than 20 people in one week. In August of that year, Hurricane Katrina devastated New Orleans, Louisiana, in the USA. One month later, Hurricane Rita – the fourth most intense Atlantic hurricane ever recorded – caused $10 billion (around £7 million) in damage on the US Gulf Coast. All of the wild weather of July and August occurred in a year that began with a deadly ice storm in New England, USA, during which 200km/h winds had shut down nuclear plants in Scandinavia and cut power to hundreds of thousands of people in Ireland and the UK.

In 2007, former vce president of the United States Al Gore (above) shared the Nobel Peace Prize with the Intergovernmental Panel on Climate Change.

## SWIFT ACTION

In September 2005, an important meeting called the Clinton Global Initiative, led by former US president Bill Clinton, was held in New York City, USA. Climate change was one of the key issues.

Speakers explained how research indicates that extreme weather conditions, such as Hurricanes Katrina and Rita, are a result of global warming. They demanded that governments around the globe take urgent action.

We need to think about how we can preserve the Earth and reduce global warming. Various fossil-fuel-reducing measures, including wind farms, are being developed.

Protests about global warming, like this one in Japan, take place all over the world. The people in the protests are calling on governments to change their policies.

## ARE WE IN TIME?

Most scientists agree that we should not wait to find out for sure what causes global warming before we do something to change it. Taking action to reduce the amount of greenhouse gases added to the atmosphere is called the 'precautionary principle'. We should decrease the burning of fossil fuels to lessen the amount of carbon dioxide in the air. Because carbon dioxide lasts for so long in the atmosphere, a reduction

▶ ▶ www.coolkidsforacoolclimate.com/Explained/KyotoProtocol.htm

in carbon-dioxide emissions takes many decades to have a noticeable effect on climate.

## GOVERNMENT ACTION

At a meeting in Kyoto, Japan, in 1997, 38 industrialized nations agreed to reduce their carbon-dioxide emissions and five other heat-absorbing gases to at least 5.2 per cent below 1990 levels by 2010. This became known as the Kyoto Protocol. Although the plans put forward at this meeting have not been fulfilled, they show that many countries have an interest in climate change. Kyoto was based on following the precautionary principle.

This image is from climateprediction.net, which harnesses idle time on personal computers owned by the public. Scientists use this spare computer time to investigate climate scenarios.

**climate**prediction **.net**

This globe shows your climate model running
Model date and time: 12/09/1922 21:30

| | |
|---|---|
| Almos Model Time | 21:30 |
| Almos Model Date | 12/09/1922 |
| Hours Elapsed | 0033:29:40 (2.61 s/TS) |
| Timestep | 46195 of 4147560 |
| zoom in to view... | |

## A CAREER IN SCIENCE

Dr Tom Wigley currently holds a senior scientist position with the National Center for Atmospheric Research in Colorado, USA, and was formerly the director of the Climatic Research Unit at the University of East Anglia in Norwich, UK. He interprets past climate changes and makes projections for future changes, with a view to detecting human influences.

## A DAY IN THE LIFE OF ...

Dr Wigley develops and uses computer models to predict probable long-term increases in the Earth's temperature. His predictions show the potential dangers of continued growth in the burning of fossil fuels. He also considers cases where actions are already being taken to reduce fossil-fuel emissions. These experiments show how much – and how rapidly – we must reduce these emissions in order to keep future climate change at a tolerable level.

## THE SCIENTIST SAYS ...

"Scientists are explorers in knowledge space, always striving to see linkages between different subjects in order to improve their understanding and so see further into the future. Nothing can be more important than this in the study of global warming, where our activities today will affect generations in the future, and our attempts to make this future brighter require improving our knowledge and understanding of the environment today."

# ENVIRONMENTAL SCHEMES

The Kyoto Protocol is an agreement between 183 countries to reduce their production of greenhouse gases. Voted on in Japan in 1997, it came into force in February 2005 when Russia joined. Each country has a different target for reducing their carbon-dioxide emissions, based on their industrial and financial situations.

## DEBATES AND DEVELOPMENTS

All countries involved with the Kyoto Protocol need to meet their targets, but some have started to question if it is the correct solution after all. Australia and the USA, for example, signed up but refused to ratify it. The Australian and US governments doubt the computer-model predictions, and believe that reducing greenhouse gas emissions will cause too much financial hardship in their countries without sufficiently benefiting the environment. They say that they are involved in other schemes to cut fossil-fuel emissions. Developed countries rely on fossil fuels for power, but some countries use more than others. For instance, about 25 per cent of all $CO_2$ emissions come from the USA. And China could overtake the USA as the world's biggest producer of $CO_2$ unless it resists becoming a heavy fossil-fuel user.

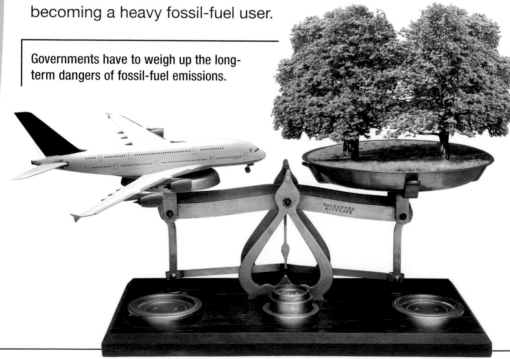

Governments have to weigh up the long-term dangers of fossil-fuel emissions.

▶ ▶ www.pewclimate.org/global-warming-basics/kidspage.cfm

Thousands march through the streets of Montreal, Canada, to protest against global warming in 2005.

## TRADING CREDITS

Some nations are reducing their greenhouse-gas emissions by more than they agreed. They can sell 'carbon credits' to countries that still have not reached the desired levels. This is called 'emissions trading'. The European Union Greenhouse Gas Emission Trading Scheme (EU ETS) allows this, and the Kyoto Protocol has a similar arrangement. Richer countries can also 'buy' the $CO_2$ allowances of other countries.

This is called the 'clean development mechanism' and is meant to reward industrialized nations and companies that give equipment and money to developing nations to help them to reduce their use of fossil fuels.

# INVESTIGATING THE EVIDENCE: HEALTH AND CLIMATE

**The investigation:** In 2009, a meeting of Commonwealth health ministers in Geneva, Switzerland, looked at the relationship of health and climate change.

**The scientists:** The study was led by Professor Sir Andrew Haines of the London School of Hygiene and Tropical Medicine (LSHTM) in the UK. Potential threats include heatwaves and flooding, patterns of infectious diseases, and hundreds of thousands of people being displaced by water scarcity and rising sea levels.

**Collecting the evidence:** The scientists are researching how climate change affects people living in developing countries and what can be learned from sustainable development and options for greenhouse gas limitations in large developed countries.

**The conclusion:** Four sectors are being studied: energy, transport, the built environment, and food and agriculture. An international team, led by the LSHTM, is modelling the impacts of policies aimed at reducing greenhouse gas emissions.

The WWF 'panda' balloon flies over the River Guaiba in Porto Alegre, Brazil. More than 100,000 environmental activists attended the World Social Forum there in 2005.

## TOMORROW'S SCIENTISTS

The impacts of climate change will become disastrous if average global temperatures increase by even 2°C. So it is vital that we find alternatives to fossil fuels and develop new technologies that will benefit the environment. Today, products to reduce the use of fossil fuels, such as energy-efficient cars, washing machines and refrigerators, are being researched.

## NEW TECHNOLOGIES

In 1969, staff and students at the Massachusetts Institute of Technology (MIT), USA, who were concerned about the incorrect use of science and technology in society founded the Union of Concerned Scientists (UCS). The UCS and other scientists say that we have the technology and inventiveness to reduce greenhouse-gas emissions – we just have to put them into practice across the world and built a better future.

▶ ▶ www.worldwildlife.org/climate/index.cfm

Some large fuel companies sponsor research activities at leading universities around the world. Among their ventures are a three-year research programme at Stanford University in California, USA, a five-year programme at Imperial College, London, UK, and a ten-year programme at the Chinese Academy of Sciences/Tsinghua University to develop new 'clean' energy technologies for the world. The World Wildlife Fund (WWF) is an organization that aims to limit and reduce $CO_2$ emissions around the world. It has formed two pioneering schemes: Climate Savers, for business and industry, and PowerSwitch!, for power companies and providers.

This scientist is investigating different strains of algae. These microorganisms convert $CO_2$ into sugars, and can be processed to produce edible oil and biodiesel, dried as a fertilizer or animal feed, or burned as an organic fuel.

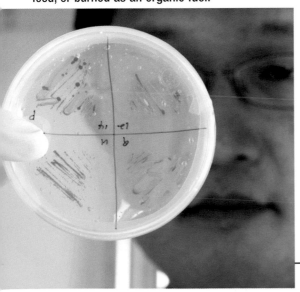

# INVESTIGATING THE EVIDENCE: HOW CLIMATE SAVERS IS HELPING

**The investigation:** The WWF hopes to show that companies concerned with the future are committed to researching and developing new technologies in order to reduce the world's dependence on fossil fuels.

**The scientists:** Scientists at the WWF address climate change on three fronts: influencing climate policy, joining with powerful partners and protecting against future climate-change impacts.

**Collecting the evidence:** WWF partnerships demonstrate that there are cost-effective company solutions to reducing greenhouse gas emissions. Companies involved include Johnson & Johnson, IBM, Nike, Polaroid, Sagawa (Japan), Lafarge (France), Tetra Pak (Sweden) and Novo Nordisk (Denmark). Power companies and public power providers account for 37 per cent of $CO_2$ emissions. WWF's seven PowerSwitch! partners will use cleaner energy by 2020.

**The conclusion:** These companies and others are exploring new technologies to develop more efficient ways of producing energy without using fossil fuels. All companies involved are committed to developing cleaner, more efficient energy products.

# EVERLASTING ENERGY?

Even if global warming were not an issue, fossil fuels are running out. There are enough left to last only a few hundred years. The IPCC say that the cost of reducing greenhouse-gas emissions is lower than imagined and that with a concerted effort, we can reduce half of our fossil-fuel emissions by 2020. Renewable resources are needed that will not run out or fill the atmosphere with $CO_2$, but so far, all have drawbacks.

1. Wind power – cheap to produce, pollution free and readily available. Wind farms provide energy without producing $CO_2$, but take up huge areas of land and may harm wildlife.

2. Hydropower, or water power – cheap and clean, but can destroy animal habitats and take up too much space.

3. Solar energy – can be converted into heat and electricity. Its major problems are the irregular way it arrives at the Earth's surface and the large area needed to collect it at a useful rate.

Renewable energy technologies include solar panels that harness heat from the Sun.

▶ ▶ www.eia.doe.gov/kids/energyfacts/sources/renewable/solar.html

4. Geothermal energy – produced by tapping into the heat of Earth's **core**. It takes a long time to be replaced. The consequences of using it are not fully known.

5. **Biomass** – uses plant and animal wastes to produce fuels such as methanol, natural gas and oil. It is cheap, but collecting sufficient quantities can be difficult, and when it burns, it produces greenhouse gases.

6. Nuclear energy – fossil fuels are used in mining and processing the nuclear fuel uranium. Many people are concerned about its cost and safety, including the disposal of nuclear waste, which might be as harmful to the environment as $CO_2$.

## A CAREER IN SCIENCE

Professor Saffa Riffat holds the chair in sustainable energy technology and is the head of the Institutes of Sustainable Energy Technology and of Building Technology at the University of Nottingham, UK. His research on **sustainable technology** and **ecobuildings** is internationally renowned.

## A DAY IN THE LIFE OF …

Professor Riffat has led several research projects to develop new sustainable products and services. As an important part of this work, he has established several unique buildings called Sustainable Life Laboratories. Inside these structures, Professor Riffat evaluates the economic and environmental impacts of renewable energy systems. A family lives in each house and uses renewable or energy-saving devices while Professor Riffat's team tests the effects.

## THE SCIENTIST SAYS …

"Much of the research carried out in the Sustainable Life Laboratories has focussed on the use of new and renewable energy technologies, such as wind turbines, ground-source heat pumps, fuel cells and solar-powered air-conditioning."

## PLANET UNDER PRESSURE

If overuse of fossil fuels and deforestation are damaging the climate, what we do today may determine how long the ice caps survive – even though it will still take several centuries for them to disappear completely. Wildlife and plants, less equipped to adapt than humans, could be affected much sooner.

If we do not change the future, global warming may cause a rise in sea levels across the world.

## FUTURE CHALLENGES

Scientists are not sure how much temperatures will increase or whether global warming is a natural occurrence that will happen no matter what we do. The future is uncertain – some places may become much warmer, while others may change little, or even become cooler. Gases do not stay still, so countries with the largest greenhouse

gas emissions will not necessarily suffer the biggest climate changes. It is also impossible to predict which plant and animal species will die out – it depends on which ones adapt best.

## HOW CAN WE HELP?

Scientists are developing methods of converting 'clean' energy into power, such as hydrogen fuel cells for cars. Other less conventional solutions include deflecting the Sun's rays, fertilizing oceans with iron to stimulate the growth of algae that consume $CO_2$ and burying greenhouse gases under the sea. More countries are joining the Asia-Pacific Partnership on Clean Development and Climate, which is committed to developing environmentally friendly technologies. We all need to reduce our use of fossil fuels. We can walk short journeys rather than drive; turn off lights, computers and TVs when we are not using them; and reduce our use of products containing palm oil or hardwood, which are taken from rainforests. Meeting the growing world's needs while reducing greenhouse gases is one of the biggest challenges that humans face.

Riding bikes instead of driving cars that burn fossil fuels can help to save the environment. It is also a much healthier activity!

**aerosol** a particle suspended in the air that has the potential to cool or warm the planet.

**algae** tiny rootless plants that grow in water

**asthma** a tightening of the airways that lead to the lungs, resulting in shortness of breath

**atmosphere** the layer of gases that surrounds Earth, stretching about 1,000 km into space

**bedrock** the solid rock under soil, sand or clay

**biomass** organic material such as vegetation that is burned to produce energy

**buoy** a floating object that stores equipment and guides ships

**carbon dioxide (CO$_2$)** a gas that occurs naturally in the atmosphere and that is essential for life; it is also produced when plants die and decay and when forests and fossil fuels are burned

**CFCs** chlorofluorocarbons; a group of gases, including fluorine, chlorine and carbon, used in various products, such as fridges and air-conditioning units

**climate** the average weather of an area over a period of time

**condense** to cause a gas or vapour to turn into a liquid

**coral reef** a colourful undersea ridge made up of colonies of tiny marine animals with hard, stony skeletons

**core** the hot, semi-liquid centre of the Earth

**deforestation** the clearance of large areas of forest

**ecobuilding** a structure designed to be used in a way that does not harm the environment

**ecosystem** a natural system of plants and animals where species interact with one another and their surroundings

**erosion** the wearing away of Earth's surface by wind, water and waves

**evaporate** to change a liquid into a vapour

**fossil fuel** a non-renewable energy source, such as coal, oil and natural gas, that is formed from the remains of fossilized plants and animals

**glacier** a huge mass of ice formed by melted snow, ice and rock debris

**greenhouse effect** the way that Earth's atmosphere traps warmth from the Sun, caused by gases in the atmosphere, such as carbon dioxide, water vapour and methane

**greenhouse gas** a gas, such as carbon dioxide, that traps heat from the Sun in Earth's atmosphere

**Gulf Stream** a warm ocean current of the North Atlantic Ocean that strongly influences the climate of northwest Europe

**hemisphere** each half of Earth, divided by the equator

**ice sheet** a vast mass of ice that can be several kilometres thick – also called an ice cap

**Industrial Revolution** the period of time in the late 18th and early 19th centuries that led to the mass production of goods in factories

**Little Ice Age** a cold period that lasted from around 1400 to 1900 in Europe, North America and Asia

**marine ecologist** a scientist who studies ocean life and environment

**mesosphere** the region of Earth's atmosphere between 50–80 km above the planet's surface

**non-renewable resource** a material that cannot be replenished

**ozone layer** the thin layer of gas that filters out harmful ultraviolet radiation from the Sun

**permafrost** permanently frozen ground in cold parts of Earth

**photosynthesis** the process by which green plants use sunlight to make nutrients from $CO_2$ and water

**precipitation** all forms of water that fall from the sky, such as rain

**radiation** energy that is transmitted in the form of rays, waves or particles

**radiosonde** a balloon that measures weather high up in the atmosphere

**rawinsonde** a radiosonde that is tracked by radar

**species** a group of living things with similar characteristics

**stratosphere** the layer of Earth's atmosphere 50km above the planet's surface

**sustainable technology** the application of science to produce techniques that are energy efficient and do not waste resources

**thermosphere** the upper layer of Earth's atmosphere

**transpiration** the process that plants undertake to give off water vapour

**troposphere** the layer in Earth's atmosphere, about 6–10km above the planet's surface, where all weather takes place

**ultraviolet** the invisible radiation from sunlight that can harm the human body

**water vapour** water in the atmosphere that takes the form of an invisible gas

**weather** the daily conditions of Earth's atmosphere in regards to temperature, wind, precipitation, etc.